Edition Schott

T0113062

The Trapp Family
Recorder Method

for Treble, Sopranino (or Bass) Recorder

A Complete Method of Instructions for the Recorder,
Including Exercises, Revisions, Trill Charts, Ornaments and
Embellishments, Duets, Trios and Quartets

Revised by
Edgar Hunt

Volume II

ED 11227
ISMN 979-0-2201-0890-7

Volume I
for Descant (or Tenor) Recorder
ED 11226

www.schott-music.com

Mainz · London · Berlin · Madrid · New York · Paris · Prague · Tokyo · Toronto
© 1976 SCHOTT MUSIC Ltd, London · Printed in Germany

CONTENTS

Copyright, 1954 by
The Trapp Family Singers
and
Magnamusic Distributors, Inc.
English revised edition

© 1976 Schott & Co. Ltd., London.

Edition 11227
ISBN 0 901938 51 3

Published by arrangement
with Magnamusic Distributors, Inc.

S. & Co. 6951

INTRODUCTION
(to the English revised edition 1975)

The recorder is today one of the most widely played musical instruments, from its use in education and in amateur circles to its position in the professional world of recitals, recording and broadcasting, in the interpretation of early music and the performance of avant-garde compositions.

The history of the recorder goes back at least to the beginning of the fifteenth century, with a hiatus in the nineteenth century — the period covered by the classical and romantic schools. Its repertory is probably more extensive than that of any other wind instrument.

The start of the recorder revival, after a century of disuse, came about in the 1920s. The complexities of modern music were driving amateur players to seek simpler means of expression. These they began to find in the music and instruments of the sixteenth and seventeenth centuries, the recorders among them.

Their introduction into schools began in the 1930s and has continued ever since. As a school instrument, the recorder has no equal. The child can make a simple beginning with a proper musical instrument — no need for song flutes and other toys — and can continue throughout his time at school. The adult beginner can do the same and can derive pleasure from taking part in ensembles which don't have to be difficult.

The present method grew out of the Trapp Family Music Camp at Stowe, Vermont, U.S.A. and was first published in 1953. For ten years the Trapp Family had been teaching people of all ages at these music camps and for twenty years the Trapp Family Singers had been playing recorders in concerts in the U.S.A., Canada, Central and South America, the Caribbean and in the Hawaiian Islands.

There have been countless recorder methods, most of them for school use. This Trapp Family Recorder Method can be used in school but it is even more suitable for small groups and adult classes. It can also be used for self instruction.

The present revision has been undertaken to bring it into line with recorder teaching today in Great Britain, in the use of musical terms, choice of fingerings and countless other details which are different on the other side of the Atlantic. The underlying method and musical material remains unchanged.

Chesham Bois   Edgar Hunt
1975

ACKNOWLEDGMENTS

I would like to express my appreciation for the help and encouragement given to me in the writing of this method. In my own Family, Father Franz Wasner and my brother Werner Trapp wrote most of the two-part settings, and all of the Family helped greatly as they always do. In addition, many others were of great assistance, of whom I would like to mention Mrs. Allston Dana, Mr. and Mrs. Harold Peterson, Professor Maximilian Albrecht, and last but not least, Mr. Theodore Mix, president of Magnamusic Distributors, Inc., the original publisher. Their contributions, suggestions, and work were an inspiration most gratefully received.

Maria Trapp

ENJOY YOUR RECORDER

We have not the slightest doubt that you will enjoy your recorder. It will become a companion to you, a means of expression that will give you much satisfaction, and it will prove a bridge of common interest between you and many others as you meet them and explore music together.

We urge you, as a beginner, to seek others now. Learn with them. Play together and help each other when one has difficulty in some note or passage. Learning by one's self is easy and pleasurable — but learning with others can be twice as enjoyable.

For this reason, we have included many duets in the Lessons. Even if you study alone, practise and master both parts. This will help you later when you play with others. In the Descant Method, most second Descant parts are within the range of a Treble Recorder. In the Treble Method, most second Treble parts are within the range of a Tenor recorder. Thus, your choice of friends and other instruments is widened while learning.

BUYING A RECORDER

The recorder is a musical instrument and not a toy.

Take your time and choose the best you can afford. The recorder must be in tune, pleasing to your ear, with both high and low notes responding easily, and the tone clear. Some prefer a brighter, some a softer tone. The extra time spent in choosing a really good recorder will repay you in the end. See that the recorder you are buying conforms to "English" (= Baroque) fingering.

The term "English" fingering refers to the size and position of the finger holes and other details of design which make it a fully chromatic instrument like the Baroque (18th cent.) recorders on which it is based. There is another system known as German fingering which originated in an attempt to simplify the fingering of the note B♭. It did that, but made it very difficult to play a good B♮. This German fingering is not used in England and, to avoid confusion, will be ignored in this book.

Baroque fingering is the authentic fingering of recorders before, during and since the Baroque period in history, and until about 1926, the only fingering.

REGULAR AND ALTERNATIVE FINGERINGS

There is a fingering for each note which gives the best pitch and is most often used in playing the recorder. We call this the "regular" fingering, and learn it first.

A few notes have "alternative" fingerings, which are also listed. These are of three types, and are explained in each case where they appear.

(1) An "alternative" fingering is one which produces the same note as the "regular" fingering, but may be easier to use when the previous or the following note is very different from the "regular" fingering of this note. Thus, in going up the scale through a certain note, the "regular" fingering may prove the easier. Coming down, the "alternative" may be the easier. Each case is explained in the text.

(2) Another type of "alternative" fingering is given, in a very few cases, because of the difference in makes of recorders. For instance, an "alternative" fingering is given in Lesson VI with the caution to use it only if your particular recorder does not sound true using the "regular" fingering. Such fingerings should not be necessary in a well-made recorder.

(3) Trill fingerings (complete chart of these may be found directly after the "Exercises") are in some cases "alternative" fingerings, too; but only because in playing a trill absolute accuracy of pitch is less important than ease and speed.

CARING FOR YOUR RECORDER

A new wooden recorder should be oiled before using it for the first time. Take the instrument apart at the joints and oil the inside of each part with a mop dipped sparingly in woodwind oil. Be careful not to oil the aperture (or opening) nor the block (plug). (See "Parts of the Recorder" on inside back cover). Let the oil dry for twelve hours, then rub off the surplus and your new instrument is ready to be played. Occasional oiling (three or four times a year) is good for the preservation of the instrument. Do not oil after playing until it is completely dry.
Never leave the recorder near heat, radiators, or in the sunlight.

Before Playing: Warm your instrument. Hold it with your hands until it is thoroughly warm. Your recorder must be warm when you start playing to protect the wood against cracking. It also helps to keep moisture from forming in the mouthpiece which blurs the tone.

During Playing: Blow firmly without overblowing. Overblowing produces a harsh tone and will eventually ruin the instrument in the higher range. If you blow too gently the tone will be dull and lifeless.
A new wooden recorder should be broken in gradually, and not played for more than a few minutes a day for the first two or three days, gradually increasing the playing time.
The upper notes require even more gradual breaking in. Spend a few practice sessions on each upper note, starting with the "G".
In the narrow opening between block and mouthpiece, moisture sometimes collects and blurs the tone. In this case place the soft part of your fingertip across the aperture and blow sharply.

After Playing: Dry your instrument. Take your recorder apart and wipe out the inside of each section gently with a dry mop, again being careful not to touch the block nor aperture of the mouthpiece. Let it dry completely before putting it away in its case or box.

HOLDING YOUR RECORDER

With The Fingers:

LEFT thumb covers the hole in the back (thumb hole)
      1st (index) finger covers 1st hole in the front
      2nd (middle) finger covers 2nd hole in the front
      3rd (ring) finger covers 3rd hole in the front

RIGHT 1st finger covers 4th hole in the front
      2nd finger covers 5th hole in the front
      3rd finger covers 6th hole in the front
      4th finger covers 7th hole in the front

Use the pads of the fingers, and not the tips, to cover the holes.

With The Arms:

Be relaxed and natural.

Hold your arms at a comfortable angle away from your body so that the recorder is held as in the illustration. Practise this in front of a mirror.

When fingers of the right hand are not in use for playing, place the little finger between the sixth and seventh hole, with the thumb on the back of the instrument between the fourth and fifth hole, which helps to balance the recorder.

Each finger should play only the holes indicated for it, as listed above.

The Lips:

Hold the mouthpiece between your lips in front of the teeth. Close your lips around the top of the mouthpiece in a relaxed and comfortable position, opening them only to breathe at the end of a phrase or at the breathing marks indicated by a comma above the staff.

PLAYING THE RECORDER

Blowing:

There are three stages in producing a note:

1. The Attack or start.
   To start a note you use your tongue as if saying "du". This attack is necessary to give the tone a clear and distinct start. This is called tongueing. Every note is tongued unless it is connected to the preceding note by a slur.

2. Blowing.
   Blow firmly and support your breath as you do in singing. Sustain the same pressure throughout to keep your pitch.
   The more pressure, the higher or sharper the pitch.
   The less pressure, the lower or flatter the pitch.
   Even, steady blowing will make your recorder a singing instrument.

3. Closings.
   To end or close your note, bring your tongue against your teeth for a "D" which remains unpronounced. It will be indicated in the lessons like this: Đ.

Finger Action:

The three rules of action for the fingers are:

1. Come down like a hammer.

2. Hold lightly for the length of the note.

3. Release quickly.

Each finger should close only the holes indicated for it, and when a finger is not in use, it should be held directly above the hole (except for the right-hand little finger which helps to support the recorder).

To play the recorder well you need co-ordination of tongue and fingers, accurate fingering, good breath control, and musicianship.

S. & Co. 6951

SYMBOLS USED IN MUSIC NOTATION

The following is not intended as a substitute for a teacher, for it is neither complete nor self-explanatory. It is to be used as a reference page to help you remember some of the symbols we use in writing music.

The Shape of Notes and Rests

The relative duration (length of time) of a note or rest is indicated by its shape. Although you cannot tell the actual duration of a note by its shape alone, you can tell how it compares with the other notes in the same composition. The following chart will show these relationships:

Each note is twice as long as the note beneath it.

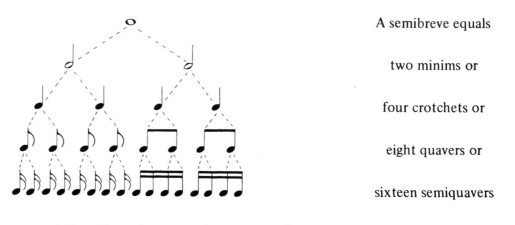

A semibreve equals

two minims or

four crotchets or

eight quavers or

sixteen semiquavers

The same relationships exist among the corresponding rests:

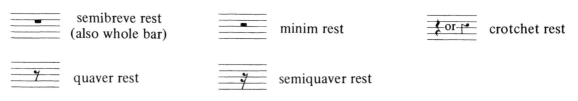

A dot placed after a note *adds one-half* of the original duration of the note.

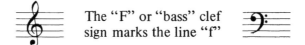

The Position Of The Notes On The Staff

The pitch, which is represented by a note, is indicated by the note's position on the staff. The higher the position on the staff the higher the pitch to be played. The clef sign placed at the beginning of the staff helps tell the names of the lines and spaces. The "G" or "treble" clef sign marks the line "g" —

The "F" or "bass" clef sign marks the line "f"

Sometimes it is necessary to cause a line or space to represent a pitch one semitone higher than it normally does. This is indicated by placing a sharp (♯) on the proper line, or in the proper space. Similarly, a line or space can represent a pitch one semitone *lower* by placing a flat (♭) on, or in, it.

When a note or a line has been sharp or flat, it is returned to the natural note by placing the natural (♮) symbol in front of the note or line. This cancels the effect of the sharp or flat.

Time Signature

At the beginning of each piece of music you will find two numbers. These help us to know how the rhythm is to be played. The upper number indicates the number of *beats* in one bar. The lower number indicates the value of each beat.

Examples:

$\frac{4}{4}$ or **C** — 4 beats in one bar
— each beat is a crotchet

$\frac{3}{4}$ — 3 beats in one bar
— each beat is a crotchet

$\frac{2}{2}$ or **¢** — 2 beats in one bar
— each beat is a minim

$\frac{6}{8}$ — 6 beats in one bar
— each beat is a quaver

Miscellaneous Symbols

The music between the two pairs of dots is to be repeated.

Pause ⌐·⌐ ⌒ The note or rest over which this sign is placed is to be held for a somewhat longer time than its usual value. It is also sometimes used to indicate the end of a piece.

D.C. — Da Capo The music is to be repeated from the beginning until either the pause (⌒) or the FINE (end) is reached.

D.S. — Dal Segno The music is to be repeated from the *sign* (𝄋) until either the pause or the FINE is reached.

8va------------------ The music under the dotted line is to be played one octave higher than written.

⌐1 ⌐2 First and second time bars are a shortened way of indicating that a *repetition* is to occur which will not use the same ending twice.

Example:

Written:

Played:

LESSON I

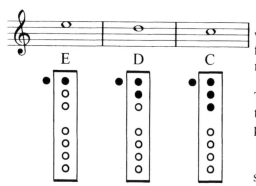

E   D   C

The first lesson is most important. Here you will put into practice what you have learned in the instructions given on pages 6 and 7, the fundamentals of recorder playing. Spend enough time and attention to master them thoroughly.

The first notes you learn are E, D, and C. To finger them you need only the left hand. The right hand supports the instrument as shown in the picture on page 6.

First, try the fingering of E, D, and C without blowing. The fingers should find their holes *by feeling.* Let them act as hammers.

Practise blowing and tongueing just one note (D). Start the note with "Du". The tongueing should be precise but gentle – not an explosion!

Breathe only at breath-marks (').

Du_____   Du_____   Du__ Du__   Du_ Du_   Du_ Du_Du_Du_   Du_Du_Du_Du_   Du____

Count silently   1 2 3 4   1 2 3 4   1 2 3 4   1 2 3 4   1 2 3 4   1 2 3 4   1 2 3 4

The dash after the "Du" —— is the breath-line. It should remind you to continue blowing until a new note starts, or the note is closed with a "Ɖ".

Close the notes with "Ɖ" as explained on page 7.

Du_ Ɖ   Du_ Ɖ   Du_ Ɖ   Du_ Ɖ   Du__ Ɖ   Du__ Ɖ   Du___ Ɖ   Du____ Ɖ

1   2   3   4   1   2   3   4   1   2   3   4   1   2   3   4   1 2 3 4 1 2 3 4 1 2 3 4

Du_ Du_ Du_ Du_Ɖ   Du_Ɖ   Du_ Du_   Du_Ɖ   Du___Ɖ

Fingers come down like hammers! Release fingers quickly!

Du_ Du_ Du_Ɖ   Du_ Du_ Du_Ɖ   Du_   Du_Ɖ

Did you keep blowing the entire length of the notes?

Did you close the notes?

© 1976 Schott Music Ltd, London

Das widerrechtliche Kopieren von Noten ist gesetzlich verboten und kann privat- und strafrechtlich verfolgt werden.
Unauthorised copying of music is forbidden by law, and may result in criminal or civil action.

Where is your right hand? Is it supporting the recorder?

First Duet with Teacher

Did you keep your lips closed around the mouthpiece and use your tongue to start each new note?

Take turns playing these parts:

Pupils' Duet

How was the position of your fingers?

Did you cover the holes with the soft part of your finger?

Melody from the Ninth Century

If you know your tongueing and fingering well, you are ready for Lesson II.

Remember to dry your instrument before you put it away!

      S. & Co. 6951

LESSON II

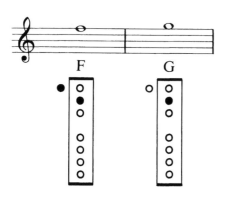

F   G

To play G, lift your thumb a short distance from the hole so that it is ready when you need to cover the hole again. Remember that your thumb must act like a hammer, too, and hit and release quickly. In playing G, you have no left thumb to hold the recorder. Your mouth, and the thumb and fourth finger of your right hand, will support and balance it.

Does your thumb hit the hole right away?

THE SLUR

The slur is a tie which connects two or a group of notes. It is played by tongueing (Du) only the first note of the slur. The following note or notes are fingered while blowing steadily.

Du____ Du____ Du____ Du__Ø Du____ Du____ Du____Ø
1   2   3   4   1   2   3   4   1   2   3   4   1   2   3   4

There may be a tendency to shorten the second note of the slur. Be sure to hold the second note for its full length, so that there is no rest between the slurs.

Here we learn a second fingering for E, indicated by EII. You have learned EI in the first lesson. The second fingering makes certain combinations of fingerings easier, and helps you to play fast passages, slurs, and trills more smoothly.

Try these combinations to see for yourself:

F   EII

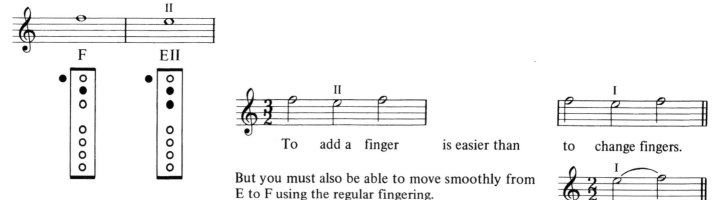

To   add a   finger   is easier than   to   change fingers.

But you must also be able to move smoothly from E to F using the regular fingering.

The rest of this lesson will be practise in playing E. In the next lesson, you will learn how to decide which fingering is better.

To change from E to G the right-hand thumb and fourth finger must steady the recorder while the left-hand thumb and first finger are exchanged for the second.

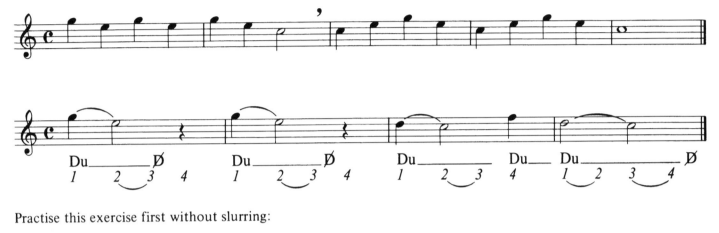

Practise this exercise first without slurring:

*Don't use the alternative E on the stronger part of a beat as it will be slightly sharp.

Slurring is a good way to check on your fingers. If you get an extra note, it is because your fingers don't find the holes right away, or are not released quickly enough, or because your tongue is not synchronized with your fingers. Keep trying until you are satisfied with the result.

Silent, Silent

German Folk Song

Is the second note of the slur as long as the first one?

S. & Co. 6951

LESSON III

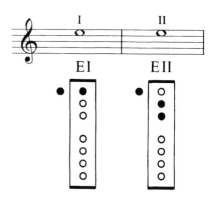

EI is fuller in tone and usually better in tune than EII. It is, therefore, preferred on sustained notes.

EII is convenient for some of the fingering combinations mentioned in Lesson II, and for slurs and trills.

Learn to know both fingerings equally well.

Here are some suggestions for deciding which fingering to use.

Use the alternative EII only when:
1. You have an unaccented E between two F's,
2. a strong F falling to a weak E, or
3. trill E – F.

Never use it on an accent (because it will be sharp) and train the fingers to move smoothly between EI and F.

From: La Volta

BYRD

Play the slurs only when you are absolutely sure of your fingering.

The Peasant and the Bear

German Folk Song

Tambour

TELEMANN

Dance Melody from Silesia

While playing with your friend, watch your tone very carefully. In a duet a singing tone is more important than a loud tone.

Sixteenth Century German Folk Song

Old German Lullaby

Now you should be able to decide for yourself when to play E I and when to play E II. Try the teacher's part in "Silent, Silent" in Lesson II. After you have decided which fingerings to use, play the duet with a friend.

* See page 9 for an explanation of $\frac{6}{8}$ time signature.

S. & Co. 6951

LESSON IV

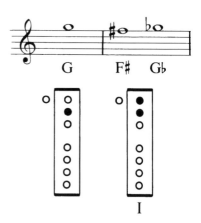

G   F#   Gb

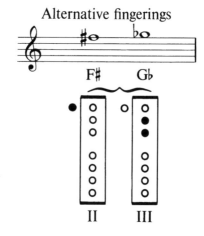

F#   Gb

II   III

F#, like G, is played with the thumbhole uncovered. Be sure to keep the thumb near the hole so that it may be easily covered when playing lower notes.

Alternative fingerings are practical to know when the regular fingering is not in tune, or to facilitate certain passages.

Alternative fingering (II) is useful in trills (E-F# and F-Gb) and certain phrases. Alternative fingering (III) is used when the regular fingering is flat on your recorder. (unnecessary on a good recorder.)

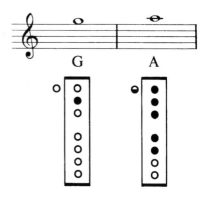

G   A

A is the first note of the second octave. It can be played at first with the thumbhole open, but the thumb should be used properly in Lesson VII and after.

A dot placed above or below a note shortens the length of the note to approximately half of its original value. Here "Dut" is pronounced crisply, as in the word "dot".

Staccato:

A line above or below a note tells you to hold the note for its full value, which brings the neighbouring notes very close together. A continuous flow of breath with a soft and fast "Du" to produce the new note will achieve the right effect of smoothness.

Du — Du — Du — Du — Ø

Exact co-ordination of fingers and tongue is needed.

Sharps or flats may be placed at the beginning of the staff instead of directly in front of each note. They affect every note which bears the same alphabetical name.

The contrasts between different degrees of long and short notes must be used to give recorder music interest and variation, since there is no great possibility for dynamics without influencing the pitch.

In recorder music, such details are seldom indicated. Most of the time they are left to the player's interpretation. In this Lesson, they are indicated so that you may learn when to play more smoothly. Later, you can apply them whenever you feel that the music asks for them.

Christmas Lullaby

German Carol

*A slur connecting two identical notes melts them together and is called a tie.

Eighteenth Century Dance

Shepherd's Music

Gipsy Dance

Watch your quavers! Are they equally long?

Austrian Folk Song

LESSON V

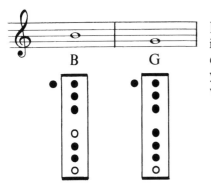

B   G

From now on you will be using the right hand. Be careful to keep both hands in position with the fingers directly above their holes so that they are ready to close them. Be sure that each hole is completely covered, for if any air leaks out you will get a squeak. Since the lower notes need less air, you should blow very carefully.

Use these semibreve exercises to practise breath control as described on page 7.

Nous allons ma Mie

French Carol

Pupil

Teacher

Canon

MORITZ HAUPTMANN (1792–1868)

A Canon, or "Round" is a melody which harmonizes with itself. The first player begins at bar (1) and when he reaches bar (2) the second player begins at (1) while the first player continues. Most canons may be repeated as many times as desired. The ending can be done in two ways: Either the different parts stop one after the other at the end of the melody, or close together with a chord at the pause. We have written out this first canon to show you how it should be played. Use the same rules for a canon with more than two parts.

Der Winter ist Vergangen

German Folk Song

Song of the Three Holy Kings

Austrian

Il était un petit navire

French-Canadian Folk Song

LESSON VI

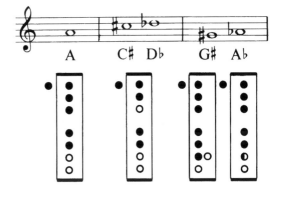

Here you find two fingerings for G♯. The second fingering is for a recorder which does not have double holes. The third finger of the right hand is stretched and leaned against the hole, as illustrated below:

Alternative fingering

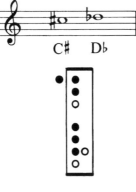

Use the alternative fingering for C♯–D♭ if the regular fingering does not sound true.

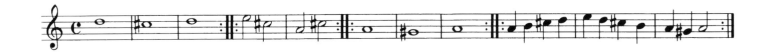

Chinese Song

S. & Co. 6951

A Bird in the Woods

German Folk Song

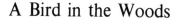

Entrez Devote Companie

French-Canadian Folk Song

Dance

AHL (1671)

Pupil I

Pupil II

Coventry Carol

English

L'Hirondelle

French-Canadian Folk Song

This is a beautiful melody. Play it and phrase it so that it sings!

Next you come to the first Revision Lesson. You can apply everything you have learned in the first six lessons when you play it. Study it, and then return to it later and do it again, not only by way of revision, but to enjoy the music!

REVISION LESSON I

Rigaudon

CHÉDEVILLE

Sweet Betsy from Pike

American Folk Song

C'est La Belle Françoise

French-Canadian

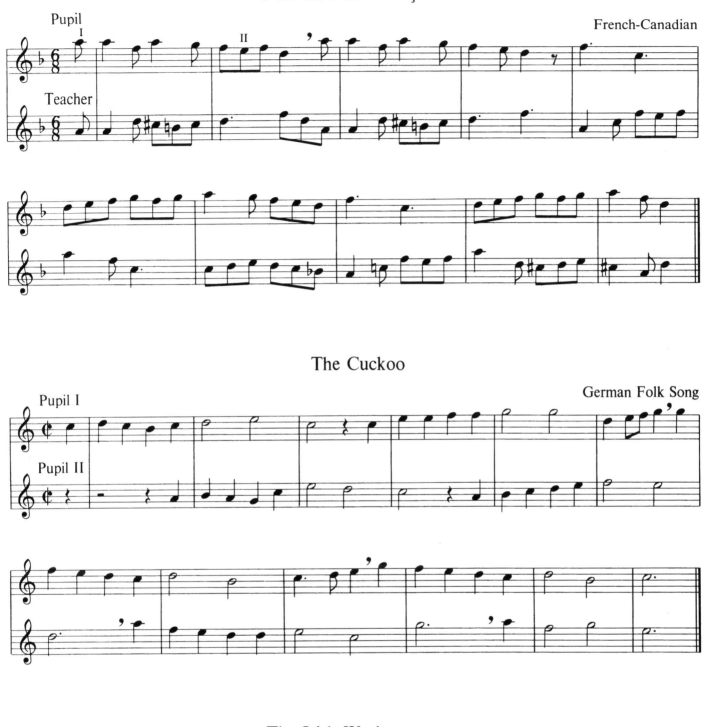

The Cuckoo

German Folk Song

The Irish Washerwoman

 S. & Co. 6951

March

CHÉDEVILLE

Five-Part Canon

PRAETORIUS

LESSON VII

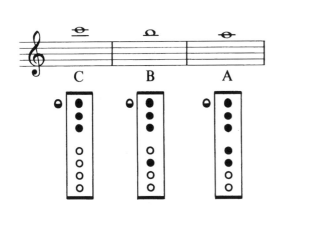

For the notes in the second, or higher octave starting with A, you tip your thumb into the thumbhole so that the thumbnail goes *into* the hole, leaving a small opening at the top of the hole. The higher the note, the smaller this opening should be. If your nail is too long, the tip of your thumb will not close the lower part of the hole tightly, and the leaking air will cause a squeak.

Upper C and A have the same fingering as low C and A, except for the thumb position.

Little Bells of Westminster

C'est Pas La Bagne

Louisiana French Folk Song

Vom Himmel Hoch

J. S. BACH

Joy to the World

HANDEL

Pupil I

Pupil II

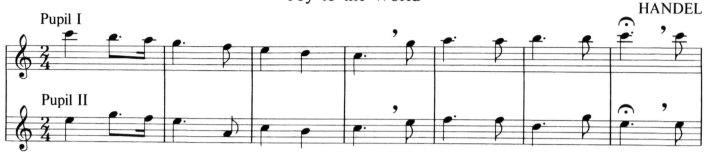

Dance

Pupil

MELCHIOR FRANK

Teacher

LESSON VIII

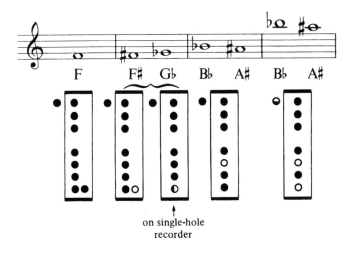

The lowest note on a recorder is always the most difficult one. You will get a good tone as soon as you are able to cover all of the holes airtight and blow steadily. Sometimes the fingers of the left hand open up and cause a squeak. Don't give up. You will master it!

Remember to use these exercises for breath control also:

A La Claire Fontaine

French-Canadian Folk Song

Be sure to play the second part, too, for it is good practise for the low F♯ and G♯.

Praise for Bread

The more time and trouble you take with difficult fingerings or passages, the faster your progress will be.

Excerpt from: Sonata II

MATTHESON

Wayfaring Stranger

American Folk Song

Rigadoon

PURCELL

From: Brandenburg Concerto No. 2

J. S. BACH

LESSON IX

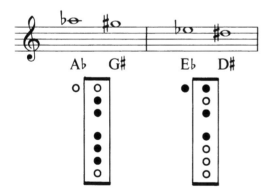

This Lesson is very important, for E♭ and A♭ often appear in recorder music. Don't be tempted to ignore it. The high A♭ is one of three notes which do not use the left-hand thumb (the others are F♯ and G), so be sure that you are supporting the recorder properly with the right-hand thumb.

Don't you notice an improvement in your tone after you have used these exercises for breath control?

Ihr Kinderlein Kommt

German Christmas Carol
Melody by JOHANN SCHULZ (1747–1800)

C'était Anne de Bretagne

French-Canadian Folk Song

Lo, We Walk a Narrow Way

Hebrew Melody

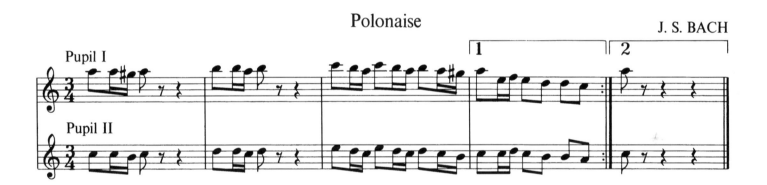

Polonaise

J. S. BACH

Pupil I

Pupil II

Good King Wenceslas

English Carol

Pupil

Teacher

If you can master these four sharps and play this carol smoothly, you can be proud of yourself!

LESSON X

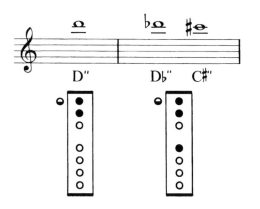

Remember that the higher the notes, the smaller the opening of the thumbhole should be. Keep the thumbnail near the upper edge of the hole. Use enough breath to produce a clear tone. All notes above C require a little more air pressure.

Every recorder has to be broken in gradually on the high notes starting with D. High-note exercises should not be played more than 20 minutes at a time for about the first six practise periods.

Retraite

English

Komm Spielmann

Austrian Folk Dance

S. & Co. 6951

C'est la Nuit

French Folk Song

Weaver's Dance

Austrian Folk Dance

*If you cannot play F♯, use D.

Gavotte

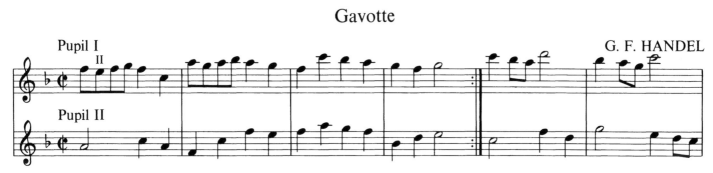

G. F. HANDEL

Here are two exercises for the ambitious student. They are taken from recorder solos by great masters, which you will enjoy in your later explorations:

Allegro from Capriccio

G. F. TELEMANN

Excerpt from: Giga, Sonata in B♭ major

LOEILLET

LESSON XI

This Lesson contains excerpts from three recorder sonatas which illustrate the high register as you will find it in original recorder music. After you master the high notes, try for expression.

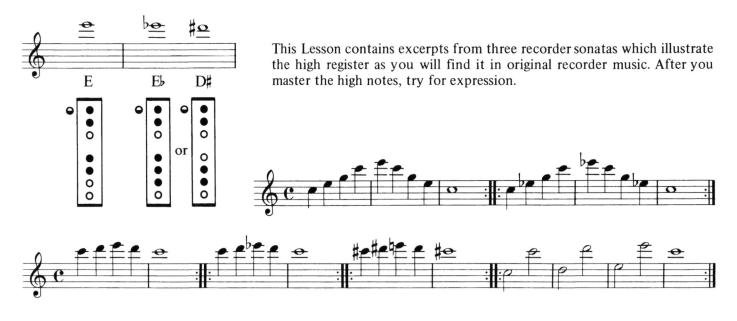

German Folksong

Rigaudon

CHÉDEVILLE

Last night the Snow fell softly

Lithuanian Folk Song

Excerpt from: Minuetto, Trio Sonata in A minor

TELEMANN

*See Trill Chart

Excerpt from: Vivace, Sonata in B♭

TELEMANN

Excerpt from: Affettuoso, Trio Sonata in A minor

Very slowly
Pupil I

TELEMANN

Pupil II

*See Trill Chart

LESSON XII

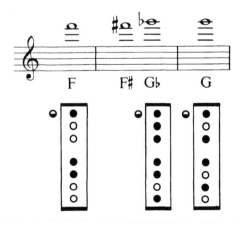

Now, in this last Lesson, you learn the highest notes. Practise them carefully and well. Remember to keep the thumbhole opening *very* small, and to blow harder than usual.

When you have finished this Lesson, go on to the Second Revision Lesson on the next pages, and the Exercises. Then you are ready to explore recorder literature. You will find that you can play the music of the old masters, and there is much music available to suit the taste of every recorder player.

Enjoy your recorder!

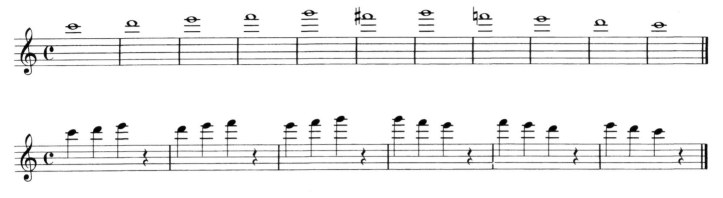

You should learn this exercise by heart and use it to warm up the high register:

Now we have taught you all of the notes on the recorder. Play the chromatic scale up and down, to see if you remember the fingerings for all of the sharps and flats. Good luck!

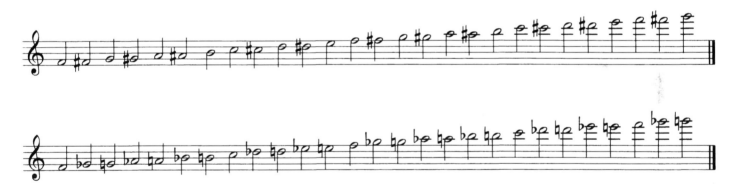

Excerpt from: Sonata II

TELEMANN

Excerpt from: Brandenburg Concerto II in F

J. S. BACH

Gigue

CORELLI

Practise this exercise before you play "Sheep may Safely Graze".

Introduction to Aria "Sheep may Safely Graze"

J. S. BACH

Slowly

S. & Co. 6951

*See preceding exercise.

REVISION LESSON II

Danish Lullaby

Folk Song

At Sunset

Finnish Folk Song

Weisst du Wieviel Sternlein Stehen

German Folk Song

Fine

D.C. al Fine

Gavotte

GIOVANNI MARTINI

Kerry Dancers

Arranged by Charlene Peterson

Irish

From: Sonata in Canon Form

TELEMANN

Light our Candles

French-Canadian

Actual Ranges of the Recorder Family

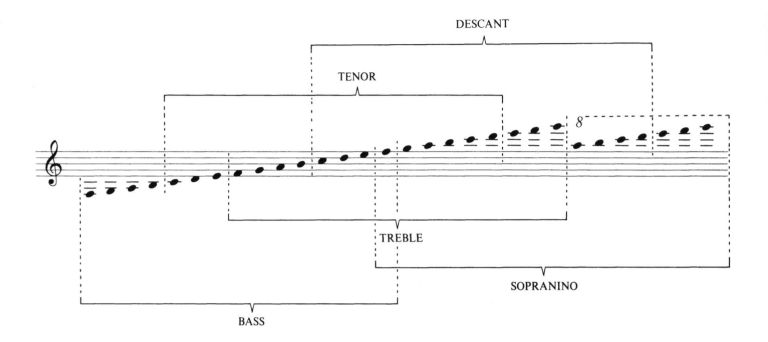

Written Ranges of the Recorder Family

Sopranino ⎫
DESCANT ⎬ Sounds one octave higher than written
Bass ⎭

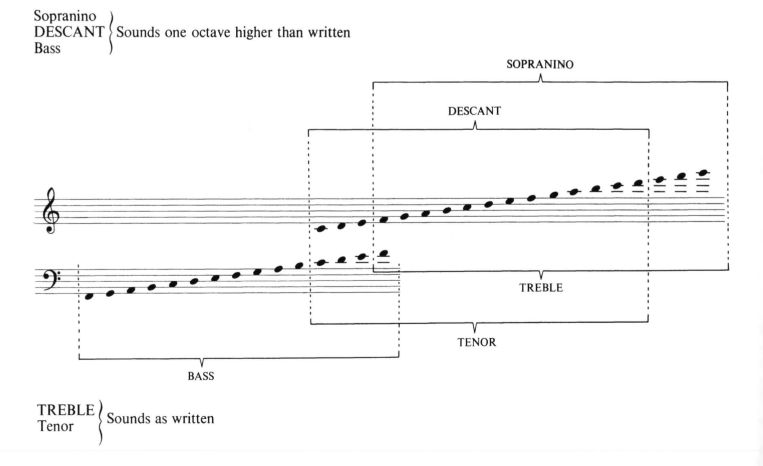

TREBLE ⎫
Tenor ⎬ Sounds as written
⎭

S. & Co. 6951

TRANSPOSITION FOR THE TREBLE RECORDER

A Treble recorder player should be able to transpose an octave up, since some DESCANT parts are also playable on a Treble recorder as long as it is within its range. Also, some recorder music is printed an octave lower than it sounds when played.

Example: Written for DESCANT Recorder

If you want to play this melody, which is written for DESCANT recorder, on the Treble recorder, you can transpose it to the correct pitch like this:

THE BASS RECORDER

The Bass recorder is not a solo instrument, but is very valuable in ensemble playing. If you play the Treble recorder and know the Bass clef, you will find it easy to play the Bass recorder, which is also an F instrument, just an octave lower.

This Canon is just to show you that the Treble and Bass recorders have the same fingering:

Canon
(for Treble and Bass Recorders)

SARTORIUS

THE SOPRANINO RECORDER

The Sopranino recorder is also fingered exactly like the Treble recorder, but sounds an octave higher. A Sopranino can take the place of a Piccolo, as in ' "Change of Guards" at the Danish Royal Palace.' Handel uses it in the opera "Rinaldo" together with two Treble recorders and a soprano voice. It will show its brilliance in imitating bird songs; Couperin's "Rossignol en Amour" and "The Bird Fancier's Delight" edited by S. Goodman.

"Change of Guards" at the Danish Royal Palace
(for Sopranino Recorder)

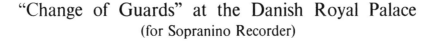

EXERCISES
To Achieve Greater Facility

Most of these exercises are phrases or excerpts from Sonatas by Old Masters, as you will find them in Recorder Literature.

Five suggestions for practising Exercise 1 in different combinations of staccato and legato.

Eight suggestions for practising Exercises 2, 3 and 5 in different combinations of staccato and legato.

Corrente

ANON.

simile

From a Sonata by LOEILLET

From a Sonata by TELEMANN

From a Sonata by TELEMANN

*simile indicates that the phrasing marked in the first bar continues for all similar bars

Phrases from Sonatas by TELEMANN

From a Sonata by HANDEL (transposed)

Gigue

TELEMANN

From a Sonata by TELEMANN

From a Sonata by TELEMANN

FINGERING CHART FOR TRILLS

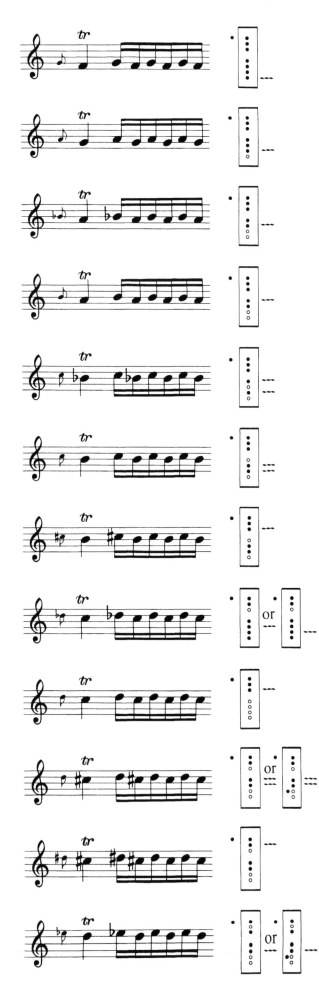

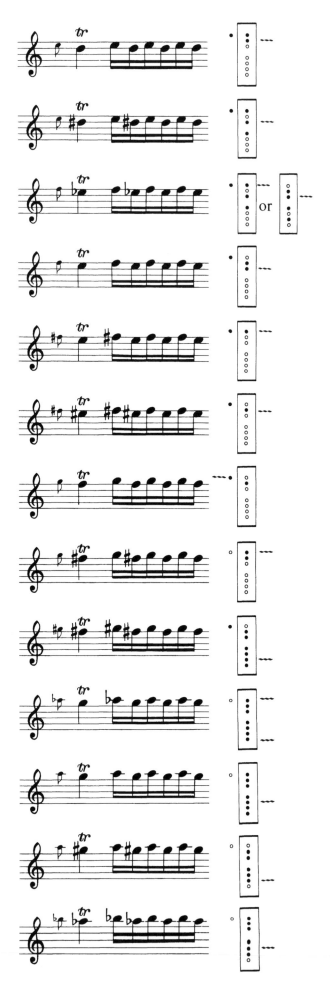

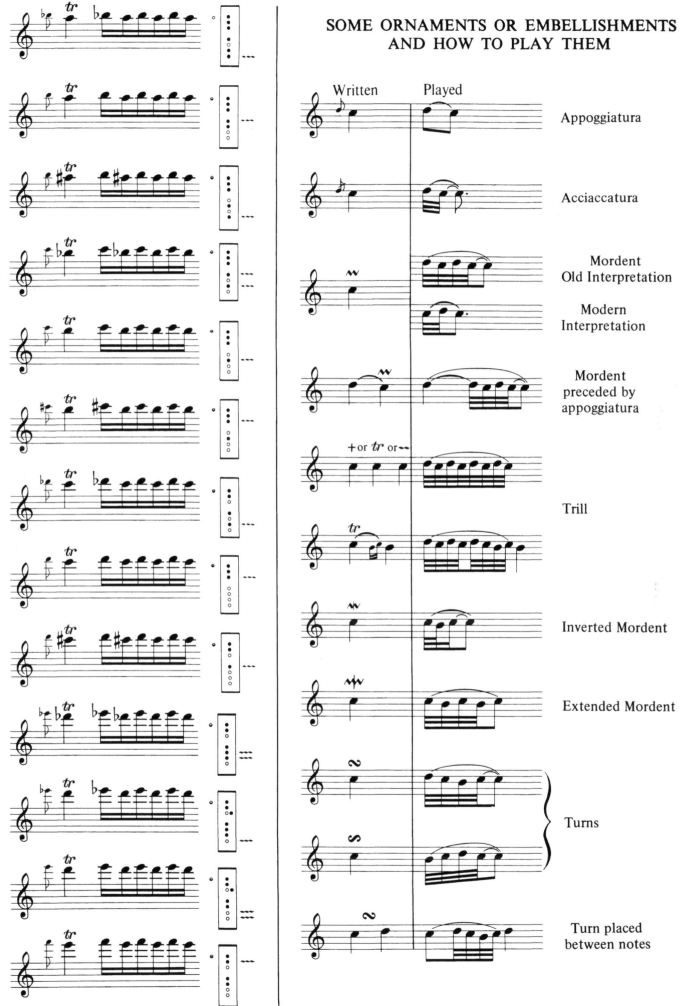

SOME ORNAMENTS OR EMBELLISHMENTS AND HOW TO PLAY THEM

Written   Played

Appoggiatura

Acciaccatura

Mordent
Old Interpretation

Modern
Interpretation

Mordent
preceded by
appoggiatura

Trill

Inverted Mordent

Extended Mordent

Turns

Turn placed
between notes

Passepied

K. FISCHER

Ozark Mountain Folk Tune

*The clef 𝄞 is used to show that the descant recorder sounds an octave higher than written.

Austrian Yodel

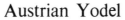

March

Austria

It was Candlemas Day

Zepperl Polka

Austrian Folk Dance

S. & Co. 6951

Les Ciseaux de La Vierge

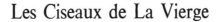

Arranged by Maximilian Albrecht

French-Canadian Folk Song

Yodel

Salzburg, Austria

Very, very slowly and solemnly

Yodel

Salzburg, Austria

Very slowly

*Treble play an octave higher

Sarabande

JOHANN PEZEL 1675

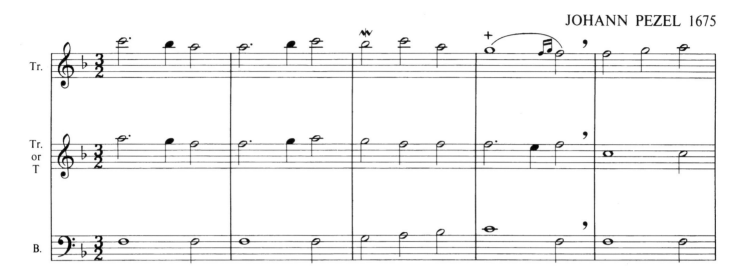

Ballo

JOHANN PEZEL 1675

Lobt Gott Ihr Christen

J. S. BACH

Meerstern ich dich Grüsse

German Pilgrimage Song

S. & Co. 6951

Schott Music Ltd, London S&Co.6951

Fingering Chart

English (Baroque) Fingered Recorders

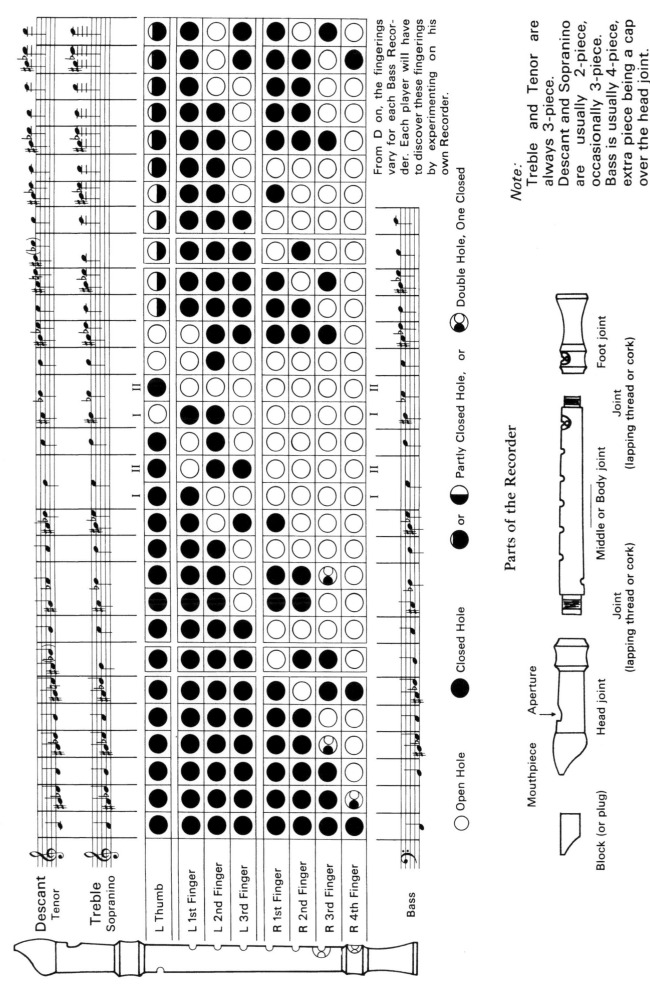

From D on, the fingerings vary for each Bass Recorder. Each player will have to discover these fingerings by experimenting on his own Recorder.

○ Open Hole ● Closed Hole ● or ◑ Partly Closed Hole, or ◉ Double Hole, One Closed

Parts of the Recorder

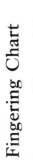

Block (or plug)

Mouthpiece Aperture

Head joint

Joint (lapping thread or cork)

Middle or Body joint

Joint (lapping thread or cork)

Foot joint

Note:

Treble and Tenor are always 3-piece. Descant and Sopranino are usually 2-piece, occasionally 3-piece. Bass is usually 4-piece, extra piece being a cap over the head joint.